Brilliant

Words by Jodi Stauffer & Ellen White
Whimsical Drawings by Thom Ricks

WOW
Productions

Published by

WOW productions

234 W. Bandera Rd. #139

Boerne, Tx 78006

thomricks@myway.com

ellenwhite@sbcglobal.net

jodi283@yahoo.com

Productions

Printed in the United States of America

Copyrighted©WOW Productions, 2011

I dedicate this book to my son,
William Stephen, you are brilliant. ~ Ellen White

I dedicate this book to Pat Hicks.
~ Jodi Stauffer

Dedicated to Tommy.
~ Thom Ricks

This book is collectively dedicated
to Vestal Elementary School in
Harlandale ISD and to the children's
section of the Patrick Heath
Public Library.

There once was an
incredibly creative
Boy,

·LINE·

who loved to draw…

But secretly he
wanted to write
because he loved
books and he thought
that maybe he'd like
to write his own book
one day… shhhh
don't tell anyone.

He tried to write with all his might
to be a good writer
but...

All he heard was

Feeling defeated,

he retreated.

He retreated

to draw...

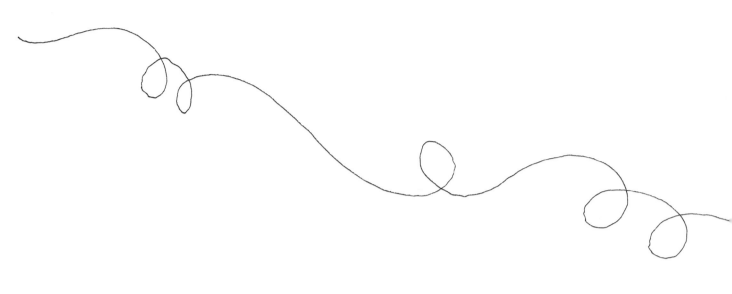

and to draw...

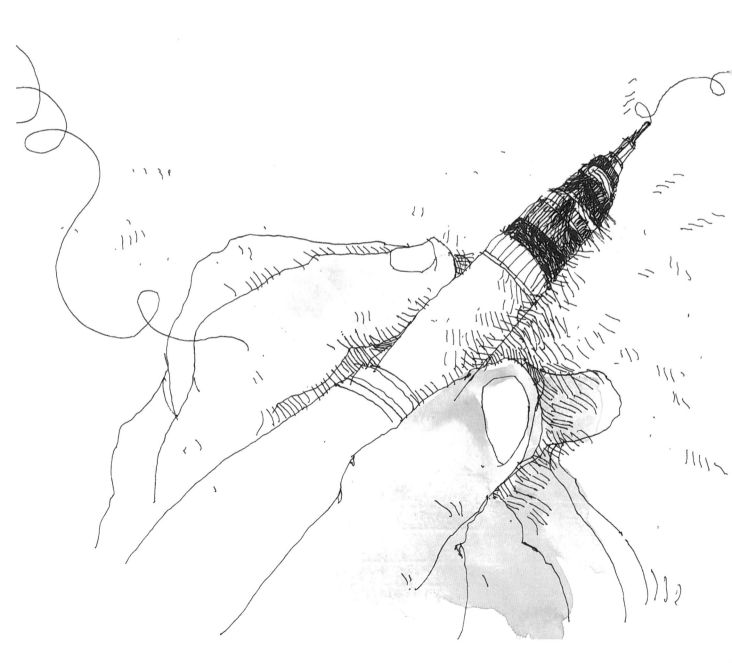

and to draw.

He was good at drawing and

when he drew he felt better.

He felt more confident.

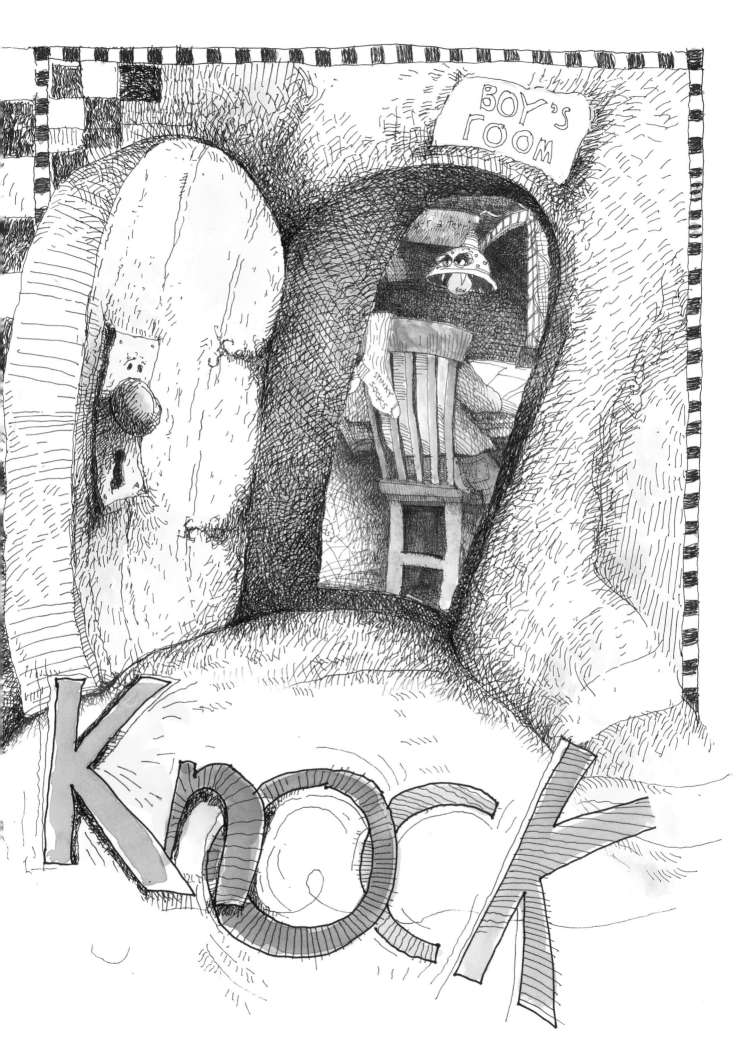

Grandfather
arrived carrying
his favorite
picture books.

As they looked at the picture
book together,
Boy noticed there were
very few words
yet it was a
fantastic story.

Grandfather reached into his pocket
and pulled out a passport which
he handed to Boy.

"Keep this with you at all times to
remind you that you can go anywhere
that your mind will take you and
you can be anything that you
dream of becoming."

Reaching into his other pocket,
he pulled out a map. He whispered,
"This is in case you get lost."

As Grandfather left he

encouraged Boy

to draw

and to write

and

to write and

to draw.

Boy decided to wait for a
word to appear,
a word that he would
WRITE.

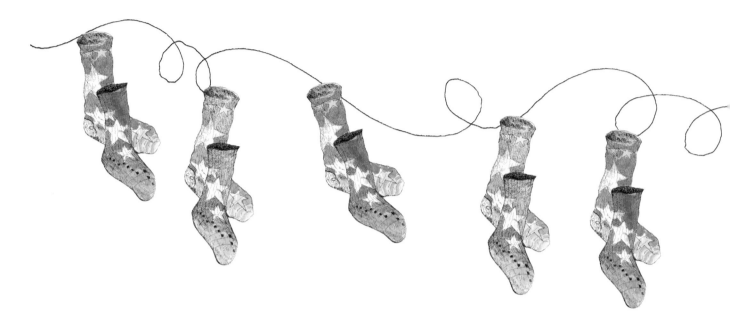

As he waited,
he drew…

ricks

and he drew

and he drew until the word
he had been waiting for
began to appear ...

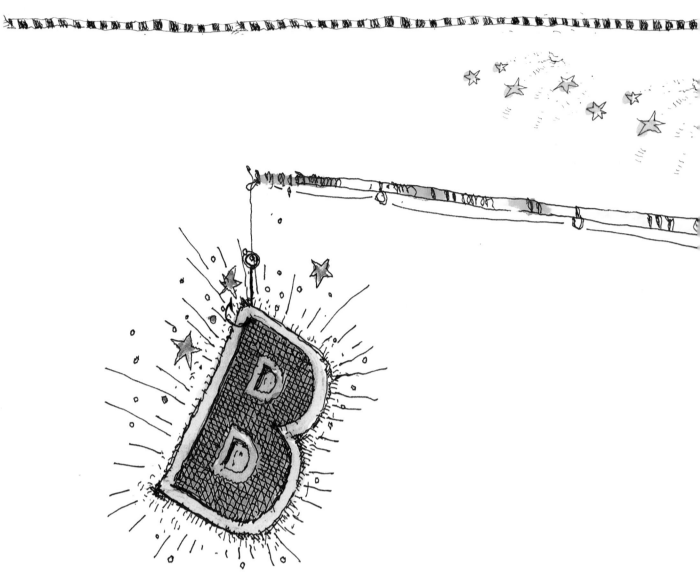

and it was...

OFFICIAL
Creativity & Wonder
PASSPORT
NUMBER: 1,2,3, GO
unlimited traveL in
the Nation of Imagination

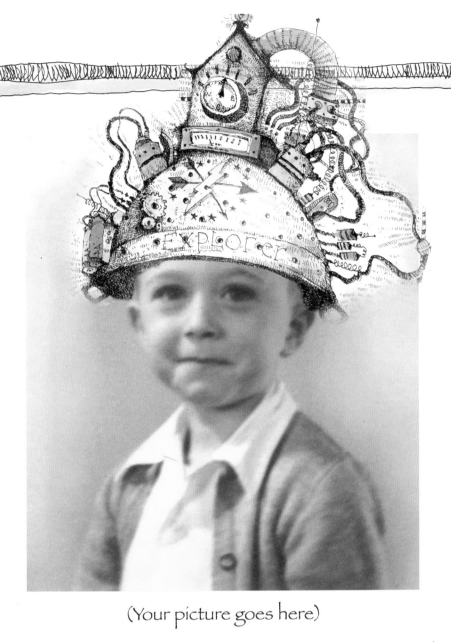

(Your picture goes here)

Roll The Credits

Gratitude and thanks go out to the following co-creators on this project:

At Vestal Elementary School in San Antonio thanks and applause go to Ms. Luna's 3rd grade class and also to Ms. Leal's G.T. class. We also appreciate the children and helpers that guided us on Career Day at Vestal Elementary School.

The Children's Circle At Celebration Circle in San Antonio.

Kim Wallace for her playful photographic excellence.

Dale Adams and his brood as well as Norman Klaunig and his clan.

Bobbie Menzel our Brilliant designer and friend.

Always grateful for our friends who encourage us and cheer us on in every project!